The Bathroom Basketball Book

By

Steve Heldt

RED-LETTER PRESS, INC.
SADDLE RIVER, NEW JERSEY

Author Acknowledgment

An English major, teacher and former radio sportstalk show host, Steve Heldt thinks he's well qualified to have written *THE BATHROOM BASKETBALL BOOK.*

He is, but there's much more to his background that lends itself to this sort of thing. And for that, I went directly to the source. Enter Clara Heldt, Steve's mom — and a nicer woman you won't meet. Mrs. Heldt says the author was potty-trained between the ages of two and three. In fact, to this day there is a crease on the family toilet seat from where little Stevie's potty-seat was fastened. (Steve, that little duck's head on the front of the seat was a real cutie pie from what your mother tells me.)

As soon as Steve was able to read, he was reading in the bathroom ... the sports pages, *SPORTS ILLUSTRATED, SPORT.* You name it, Steve read it. And, Mrs. Heldt claims, "Stevie always read with his little baseball cap on."

Little Stevie got bigger, but not big enough. A good athlete, he just wasn't tall enough to play basketball according to his mom. But read about it, he did. Like Jordan to the air and Magic to the hoop, it was Steve to the hopper.

And so goes the evolution of the man and his book.

Meanwhile, Mrs. Heldt had a favorite bathroom pastime of her own. Though she doesn't do it any more because her eyesight's not what it used to be, she thinks it might make for a good book subject. It would be appropriately called *THE BATHROOM CROCHET BOOK.*

Yours flushingly,

Jack Kreismer
Publisher

FIRST THINGS FIRST

Can you name them?

1. The first player to lead the NBA in scoring and assists in the same season.

2. The first player to score 2,000 points in a season.

3. The first player to win back-to-back playoff MVP awards.

4. The first black player drafted into the NBA.

5. The first player to score 20,000 points in his career.

6. The first player to get a quadruple double in one game.

7. The first coach to lead a team in the All-Star Game in his rookie season.

8. The first brothers to be teammates in the NBA Championship Series.

9. The first player in the NBA to have been a Rhodes scholar.

10. The first player taken in the 1979 NBA draft.

1. *Nate Archibald, Kansas City Kings, 1972-73, 34 points per game, 11.4 assists*

2. *George Yardley, Detroit Pistons, 1957-58*

3. *Willis Reed, New York Knicks, 1972 and 1973*

4. *Chuck Cooper, Duquesne, by the Celtics in 1950*

5. *Bob Pettit, St. Louis Hawks*

6. *Nate Thurmond, 1974; 22 points, 14 rebounds, 13 assists, 12 blocked shots*

7. *Ed Macauley, St. Louis Hawks, 1959*

8. *Dick and Al McGuire, New York Knicks, 1952*

9 *Bill Bradley, Princeton and the New York Knicks*

10. *Earvin "Magic" Johnson, Michigan State, by the Los Angeles Lakers*

THOUGHTS OF THE THRONE

The ABA held the first Slam Dunk Contest between halves of the 1976 All-Star Game. *Sports Illustrated* called it "the best halftime invention since the restroom."

THE TIP-OFF

1. With what team did Julius Erving begin his professional career?

2. In 1986, the Lakers had four players on the roster who had been selected with the No. 1 pick in the NBA draft. Magic Johnson (1979) and Kareem Abdul-Jabbar (Milwaukee, 1969) were two of them. Who were the other two?

3. Bob Cousy won eight consecutive assist titles. Name the guard who ended that streak.

4. Who is the only player to have been named MVP in the ABA and NBA All-Star Games?

5. The dominant play of this center caused the NBA to widen the foul lane from 6 feet to 12 feet. Can you name him?

6. Who was the No. 1 pick in the 1990 draft?

7. What innovation of the ABA remained a part of the pro game after the merger with the NBA?

8. Who was the NBA's first black head coach?

9. Name the four current franchises that were members of the ABA.

10. The Lakers and Celtics won 8 of the 10 championships in the 1980's. Who won the other two?

1. *Virginia Squires of the ABA*

2. *James Worthy (1982) and Mychal Thompson (Portland, 1978)*

3. *Oscar Robertson*

4. *David Thompson*

5. *George Mikan*

6. *Derrick Coleman, Syracuse, by the New Jersey Nets*

7. *the 3-point basket*

8. *Bill Russell, Celtics*

9. *Nets, Nuggets, Spurs, and Pacers*

10. *76ers, 1983 and Pistons, 1989*

OFF TO A GOOD START

1. These two Detroit rookies were starters in the 1982 All-Star Game.

2. He was the first to play in an NCAA final in his last collegiate season and the NBA Finals in his rookie season.

3. They shared Rookie of the Year honors for the 1970-71 season.

4. He was the Rookie of the Year in Magic Johnson's first NBA season.

5. He's the only man to win Rookie of the Year and Coach of the Year awards in his career.

6. Named Most Outstanding Player in the 1980 NCAA Tournament, he went on to become Rookie of the Year in the 1980-81 NBA season.

7. They're the only brothers named to the NBA All-Rookie team in the same season.

8. This Royal went from Rookie of the Year in 1963-64 to the MVP Award the next season.

9. He was the only overall No. 1 draft pick to be named Rookie of the Year in the 1970's.

10. His rookie season as an NBA head coach was spent as the first coach of the Los Angeles Lakers.

1. *Isiah Thomas and Kelly Tripucka*

2. *Bill Russell*

3. *Geoff Petrie and Dave Cowens*

4. *Larry Bird*

5. *Tom Heinsohn*

6. *Darrell Griffith*

7. *Tom and Dick VanArsdale*

8. *Jerry Lucas*

9. *Kareem Abdul-Jabbar*

10. *Fred Schaus*

ALMA MATER

Match the Hall-of-Fame player with the college he attended.

1.	Bob Cousy	a.	Marshall
2.	Walt Frazier	b.	LSU
3.	Nate Thurmond	c.	Providence
4.	John Havlicek	d.	West Virginia
5.	Elgin Baylor	e.	Holy Cross
6.	Hal Greer	f.	Louisville
7.	Bob Pettit	g.	Bowling Green
8.	Jerry West	h.	Seattle
9.	Wes Unseld	i.	Ohio State
10.	Lenny Wilkens	j.	Southern Illinois

Answers

1. *e*

2. *j*

3. *g*

4. *i*

5. *h*

6. *a*

7. *b*

8. *d*

9. *f*

10. *c*

HOME SWEET HOME

Name the teams that call these arenas "home".

1. The Spectrum

2. HemisFair Arena

3. Capital Centre

4. The Summit

5. Meadowlands Arena

6. Reunion Arena

7. Madison Square Garden

8. Great Western Forum

9. The Omni

10. The Palace of Auburn Hills

1. *Philadelphia 76ers*

2. *San Antonio Spurs*

3. *Washington Bullets*

4. *Houston Rockets*

5. *New Jersey Nets*

6. *Dallas Mavericks*

7. *New York Knicks*

8. *Los Angeles Lakers*

9. *Atlanta Hawks*

10. *Detroit Pistons*

SIMPLY CHARMIN'
Can you name the coach who guided the Los
Angeles Lakers to the 1972 NBA Championship
over the New York Knicks?

*Answer: His last name is pronounced the same as
the toilet paper- (Bill) Sharman.*

THE BIG DIPPER

How much do you know about Wilt Chamberlain?

1. Chamberlain was the first NBA player to win Rookie of the Year and Most Valuable Player awards in the same year. What season was it?

2. Despite winning his third straight NBA scoring title in 1961-62, Wilt was not named MVP. Who won the trophy?

3. True or false: Wilt Chamberlain won an NBA assist title.

4. Chamberlain was traded in 1968 from the 76ers to the Lakers for three players. Two of them were Darrall Imhoff and Jerry Chambers. Can you name the third?

5. During his career, Wilt the Stilt won the scoring crown 7 consecutive years. Name the player who broke the string in 1966-67.

6. Besides Chamberlain, only two other players have scored 70 or more points in a regular season game. Who are they?

7. True or false: Wilt Chamberlain never fouled out of an NBA game.

8. How many MVP awards did Chamberlain win in his career?

9. When Chamberlain led the league in scoring with a 50.4 average in 1961-62, this player was runner-up.

10. True or false: Wilt was a head coach in the ABA.

1. *1959-60*

2. *Bill Russell, Celtics*

3. *True. 1967-68*

4. *Archie Clark*

5. *Rick Barry, 35.6 points per game*

6. *David Thompson (73) of Denver and Elgin Baylor (71) of the Lakers*

7. *True*

8. *Four*

9. *Walt Bellamy with 31.6 points per game*

10. *True. San Diego Conquistadors, 1973-74*

HALL OF NAMES

Do you know the real first names of these NBA players?

1. Buck Williams

2. Dominique Wilkins

3. Magic Johnson

4. Pooh Richardson

5. J.R. Reid

6. Trent Tucker

7. Blue Edwards

8. Mark Price

1. *Charles*

2. *Jacques*

3. *Earvin*

4. *Jerome*

5. *Herman*

6. *Kelvin*

7. *Theodore*

8. *William*

SHARP SHOOTERS

1. Back in the mid-70's, this Buffalo Brave won three straight scoring titles. Name him.

2. He holds the career record for most seasons with 2,000 points or more. Who is it?

3. This player, though, set a record when he scored 2,000 points or more in eight consecutive seasons. Can you name him?

4. True or false: No member of the Celtics has ever won an NBA scoring title.

5. Name the man who sank 78 free throws in a row during the 1980-81 season.

6. Has any NBA player scored 4,000 points in a season?

7. This Hall-of-Famer once scored 64 points in a game. Yet, despite being the league's best free throw shooter, he scored only 4 of those points from the charity stripe. Who is it?

8. The largest margin of victory in a game was set by what team in a 162-99 win over Golden State in 1972?

9. The record for most free throws made in a game is 28. Wilt Chamberlain shares the record with what other player?

10. In 1968, he won the ABA's first scoring title. Who was it?

Answers

1. *Bob McAdoo*

2. *Kareem Abdul-Jabbar, 9*

3. *Alex English*

4. *True*

5. *Calvin Murphy, Houston Rockets*

6. *Yes. Wilt Chamberlain scored 4,029 points in the 1961-62 season.*

7. *Rick Barry*

8. *Los Angeles Lakers*

9. *Adrian Dantley*

10. *Connie Hawkins*

THE ROAD TO THE FINAL FOUR

How well-schooled are you on the NCAA Tournament?

1. Name the only school to win the NIT and NCAA Tournament in the same year.

2. That team faced the same school in the finals of both tournaments. Name the runner-up.

3. Between 1964 and 1969, UCLA won 5 of 6 NCAA titles. Who was champ the other time?

4. In 1960, Ohio State defeated the defending champion in the title game. Name the school.

5. They were defending champs because, in 1959, they beat a team led by a future Laker Hall-of-Famer. Who was the player and his school?

6. Dean Smith's first NCAA title as coach came in 1982 when North Carolina defeated what school?

7. He was once an assistant to John Wooden at UCLA. His team beat the Bruins in the final game. Do you know who it is?

8. Indiana finished a 32-0 season with a win over another Big Ten team in the 1976 final. Name that school.

9. His first and only title came in his last game as a coach. Who is he? What was the school?

10. This heavy underdog shot 79 percent from the field in the championship game to capture the 1985 crown. Who was it?

1. *City College of New York, 1949-50*

2. *Bradley*

3. *Texas Western, 1966*

4. *California*

5. *Jerry West, West Virginia*

6. *Georgetown*

7. *Denny Crum, Louisville*

8. *Michigan*

9. *Al McGuire, Marquette*

10. *Villanova*

ON THE JOHN
He was the head coach of the 1984 NCAA Champions as they defeated Houston, 84-75. Can you come up up with the coach and the school?
Answer: John Thompson, Georgetown

BY THE NUMBERS

Do you know them?

1. 13

2. 15 feet

3. 100 points

4. 23 feet, 9 inches

5. 6

6. 94 feet

7. 27

8. 44

9. 12

10. 60,000

10 Answers

1. *Wilt Chamberlain's uniform number*

2. *distance from basket to foul line*

3. *most points scored by a player in an NBA game*

4. *distance of 3-point line from the basket*

5. *Bill Russell's uniform number*

6. *length of basketball court*

7. *number of teams in NBA*

8. *Jerry West's uniform number*

9. *NBA roster limit*

10. *approximate number of pebbles on basketball*

KEEP YOUR GUARD UP

1. When he won the NBA scoring title in 1967-68, this Piston became the first guard to accomplish that feat in 20 years. Who was it?

2. What guard won the MVP award in 1987-88 after winning his second straight scoring crown?

3. The all-time leader in career steals, this 76er made the All-Defensive team five straight years. Name him.

4. In 1987-88, he became the first Knick since Willis Reed to win Rookie of the Year. Who was it?

5. Who was the only guard to be named MVP in the 1960's? He won it in 1963-64.

6. What Net not only led the league in assists in 1977-78, but also in turnovers?

7. He spent the last year of his career as the 41-year old player-coach of the Cincinnati Royals. Name him.

8. Rookie of the Year in 1967-68, this pearl of a player was elected to the Hall of Fame in 1989. Do you know him?

9. In his only appearance in an All-Star Game (1966), this Cincinnati guard won the MVP award. Who was it?

10. He wasn't the top rookie in 1979-80, but he was the MVP in the NBA Finals. Pull his name out of the hat.

11   Answers

1. *Dave Bing*

2. *Michael Jordan*

3. *Maurice Cheeks*

4. *Mark Jackson*

5. *Oscar Robertson*

6. *Kevin Porter*

7. *Bob Cousy*

8. *Earl Monroe*

9. *Adrian Smith*

10. *Magic Johnson*

A MAN FOR ALL SEASONS

1. He's the only player to win championships in two sports - with the 1957 Milwaukee Braves and the 1959, '60, and '61 Celtics.

2. A 14th-round pick of Seattle in the 1968 draft, this former UCLA player had better luck guarding the city in "Hill Street Blues."

3. This former Houston Rocket point guard spent off-seasons attacking the net in Professional Team Tennis.

4. The Cleveland Browns liked him enough to select him in the 1962 NFL draft, but this Buckeye spent 16 years shooting the eyes out of the basket in Boston.

5. He's the only person in both the basketball and football Halls-of-Fame.

6. These two baseball Hall-of-Famers once played for the Harlem Globetrotters. Pitch us their names.

7. He scored over 1800 points in his college basketball career at Utah State, and also played in two Super Bowls for the Cowboys.

8. This baseball All-Star and former Minnesota Gopher was drafted by the NBA and ABA.

9. This former Celtic great spent five years as commissioner of the American Soccer League in the 1970's.

10. He's the only man to coach a team in the Super Bowl and play on an NBA championship team. He played on the 1950 Minneapolis Lakers.

1. *Gene Conley*

2. *Mike Warren*

3. *John Lucas*

4. *John Havlicek*

5. *Amos Alonzo Stagg*

6. *Bob Gibson and Ferguson Jenkins*

7. *Cornell Green*

8. *Dave Winfield*

9. *Bob Cousy*

10. *Bud Grant*

WHO AM I?

1. I'm the only woman drafted by the NBA.

2. At 6'5", I'm the shortest man to win an NBA rebounding title.

3. I'm a Hall-of-Famer who made the All-NBA second team 7 times while playing for Philadelphia. But I never made first team.

4. I was the NBA MVP for 1981-82 with Houston. I was traded after that season and won the award the next year with my new team.

5. I was the first coach of the Portland Trailblazers.

6. I'm the smallest player to win an NBA scoring title.

7. I played exactly fifty thousand minutes in my NBA career after an All-American stint at the University of Houston.

8. They used me for the model in the official NBA logo. I'm the silhouetted player you see on all NBA uniforms.

9. I coached the Tri-Cities Hawks and Washington Capitols before embarking on my trip to the record book as all-time winning coach.

10. When I retired, I had more career points than any other player, yet never led the league in season scoring. My son still plays in the NBA.

1. *Lucille Harris, Delta State, by New Orleans in 1977*

2. *Charles Barkley, 1986-87*

3. *Hal Greer*

4. *Moses Malone, Philadelphia*

5. *Rolland Todd*

6. *Nate Archibald, Kansas City Kings, 1972-73*

7. *Elvin Hayes*

8. *Jerry West*

9. *Red Auerbach*

10. *Dolph Schayes*

THOUGHTS OF THE THRONE
"In basketball, it took only 20 years to go from the outhouse to the in crowd."

—Bill Russell, on how long it took from being the only black on the Boston Celtics to becoming coach and general manager of the Seattle Supersonics

SCHOOL DAYS

1. This college basketball player was the first to win the Sullivan Award as the nation's top amateur athlete. Who was it?

2. Who was the coach who replaced the legendary John Wooden at UCLA?

3. Speaking of legends and UCLA, what player took over at center when Lew Alcindor graduated in 1969?

4. Since we're filling big shoes, who succeeded Adolph Rupp as head coach at Kentucky?

5. His NCAA record for points in a game (69) stood for 21 years. Name the player and his school.

6. Who was the player who broke that record with 72 points in one game in 1991?

7. Penn and Princeton dominated the Ivy League with 17 straight titles between them. What school broke the string in 1986?

8. One of the bigger upsets in college basketball occurred in 1982 when Ralph Sampson and undefeated Virginia were upset by an NAIA school. Name it.

9. UCLA holds the record for most consecutive wins. How many?

10. Name the school that ended the Bruins' streak.

1. *Bill Bradley, Princeton, 1965*

2. *Gene Bartow*

3. *Steve Patterson*

4. *Joe B. Hall*

5. *Pete Maravich, LSU*

6. *Kevin Bradshaw, U.S. International University*

7. *Brown*

8. *Chaminade, of Hawaii*

9. *88*

10. *Notre Dame*

MULTIPLE CHOICE

1. What's the only team to win the championship one year and miss the playoffs the next season? a) 76ers b) Celtics c) Bullets d) Clippers

2. What college did former NBA center Daryl Dawkins attend? a) UCLA b) Yale c) Temple d) none of the above

3. Who was the first guard to win the MVP Award? a) Slater Martin b) Jerry West c) Bob Cousy d) Hal Greer

4. Which one didn't win Rookie of the Year? a) Magic Johnson b) Bob McAdoo c) Ernie DiGregorio d) Adrian Dantley

5. Who's the only athlete to play for NCAA, NBA, and ABA champs? a)Rick Barry b) Julius Erving c) Tom Thacker d) Tom Thumb

6. What former ABA team posted the worst record in the first season after the merger? a) Spurs b) Nets c) Nuggets d) Pacers

7. Who's the only man elected to the Hall of Fame as a player and coach? a) John Wooden b) Dean Smith c) Bill Russell d) Al McGuire

8. What school won the first NCAA final decided in overtime? a) North Carolina b) UCLA c) Georgetown d) Indiana

9. What was the first team to sweep the NBA Finals? a) Lakers b) Royals c) Celtics d) Pistons

10. Which one didn't win at least 3 consecutive NBA scoring titles? a) George Gervin b) Rick Barry c) Michael Jordan d) Wilt Chamberlain

1. *b*

2. *d. He signed out of high school.*

3. *c, 1956-57*

4. *a*

5. *c, U. of Cincinnati, Celtics, Pacers*

6. *b*

7. *a*

8. *d*

9. *c*

10. *b*

FIRST IN, FIRST OUT

The players listed below were No. 1 draft choices. Match them with the team that made the pick.

1. David Rivers, Notre Dame, 1988   a. Celtics

2. Wiley Peck, Mississippi St., 1979   b. Nets

3. Mel Davis, St. John's(NY), 1973   c. Trailblazers

4. LaRue Martin, Loyola, 1972   d. Lakers

5. Dwayne Washington, Syracuse, 1986   e. Knicks

6. Dana Lewis, Tulsa, 1971   f. Hawks

7. Norm Cook, Kansas, 1976   g. Trailblazers

8. Al Eberhard, Missouri, 1974   h. 76ers

9. Skip Harlicka, South Carolina, 1978   i. Spurs

10. Rich Laurel, Hofstra, 1977   j. Pistons

1. *d*

2. *i*

3. *e*

4. *g or c*

5. *b*

6. *h*

7. *a*

8. *j*

9. *f*

10. *c or g*

THOUGHTS OF THE THRONE

Most toilet paper makers manufacture a sheet of paper which is 4½ inches long. In an average 1,000 sheet roll, would there be enough toilet paper to go around the perimeter of a professional basketball court?

Answer: Yes. 375 feet of toilet paper would be more than ample to cover the maximum 94 foot by 50 foot court.

QUOTE, UNQUOTE

"It ain't over till..." Finish the quote by Bullets' coach Dick Motta by answering the following clues and writing the boxed letter in the corresponding space at the bottom of the page. (Hint: they're all nicknames.) We've given you the first deuce.

1	The Bad Boys	P I S (T) O N S
2.	Hondo	(H) A V L I C E K
3.	The Pearl	_ _ _ _ _ (_) _
4.	Sleepy	(_) _ _ _ _ _
5.	The Mailman	_ (_) _ _ _ _ _
6.	Jungle Jim	_ _ _ _ _ (_) _ _
7.	Clyde the Glide	_ _ _ _ (_) _ _
8.	The Dream	_ _ (_) _ _ _ _ _
9.	Air	_ _ _ (_) _ _
10.	Sir Charles	_ _ _ _ _ _ (_)
11.	The Big "O"	_ _ _ _ _ _ (_) _
12.	Hot Rod	_ (_) _ _ _ _ _
13.	Magic	_ _ _ (_) _ _ _
14.	Dr. J	_ _ _ _ _ (_)
15.	Mr.	_ _ _ _ _ (_) _

$\overline{1}\ \overline{2}\ \overline{3}\quad \overline{4}\ \overline{5}\ \overline{6}\quad \overline{7}\ \overline{8}\ \overline{9}\ \overline{10}\quad \overline{11}\ \overline{12}\ \overline{13}\ \overline{14}\ \overline{15}$

1	The Bad Boys	P I S (T) O N S
2.	Hondo	(H) A V L I C E K
3.	The Pearl	M O N R O (E)
4.	Sleepy	(F) L O Y D
5.	The Mailman	M (A) L O N E
6.	Jungle Jim	L O S C U (T) O F F
7.	Clyde the Glide	D R E X (L) E R
8.	The Dream	O L (A) J U W O N
9.	Air	J O R (D) A N
10.	Sir Charles	B A R K L E (Y)
11.	The Big "O"	R O B E R T (S) O N
12.	Hot Rod	W (I) L L I A M S
13.	Magic	J O H (N) S O N
14.	Dr. J	E R V I N (G)
15.	Mr.	R O B I N (S) O N

T H E F A T L A D Y S I N G S
1 2 3 4 5 6 7 8 9 10 11 12 13 14 15

BROACHING COACHING

1. Who was the first coach of the Milwaukee Bucks?

2. A player-coach with two NBA teams, he won a title with Seattle in 1978-79.

3. This coach "guaranteed" his team would repeat as NBA champions.

4. As a player, he was a Hall-of-Famer. As coach of the Cincinnati Royals/Kansas City Kings, he never had a winning record.

5. Coach of the Year in 1970, he brought "dee-fense" to the city where he won two titles.

6. Who was the first coach of the Phoenix Suns?

7. Despite winning nine NBA championships, he was voted Coach of the Year only once.

8. Who won NBA titles with St. Louis and Philadelphia, and an ABA crown with Oakland?

9. This man took over as head coach of the Lakers 14 games into the 1979-80 season and led them to the championship.

10. He's the coach who was replaced by the answer to question #9.

Answers

1. *Larry Costello*

2. *Lenny Wilkens*

3. *Pat Riley*

4. *Bob Cousy*

5. *Red Holzman*

6. *John Kerr*

7. *Red Auerbach*

8. *Alex Hannum*

9. *Paul Westhead*

10. *Jack McKinney*

ALMA MATER

Match the player with the college he attended.

1. Jack Twyman   a. Tennessee

2. Rick Barry   b. Georgia Tech

3. Earl Monroe   c. Syracuse

4. Frank Ramsey   d. Miami (Fla.)

5. Bernard King   e. Nevada Las Vegas

6. Dave Bing   f. Winston-Salem

7. Don Nelson   g. Michigan

8. John Salley   h. Cincinnati

9. Cazzie Russell   i. Kentucky

10. Reggie Theus   j. Iowa

1. *h*
2. *d*
3. *f*
4. *i*
5. *a*
6. *c*
7. *j*
8. *b*
9. *g*
10. *e*

THE HOT HAND

1. Four of the top 10 individual scoring performances in NBA history have occurred against this team. Name the victim.

2. Wilt Chamberlain scored more than 70 points in a game 3 times in one season. What campaign was it?

3. This player scored 73 points in the last game of the 1977-78 season, but lost the scoring title. Who was it?

4. 63 points in his final game of the year spurred this point machine to the scoring championship that same season. Name him.

5. This Hall-of-Famer scored 50 points in a four-over-time game in the 1953 playoffs, at that time a record. Who was it?

6. He once scored 69 points as a collegian. His best in the NBA was a 68-point effort in 1977. Do you know who it was?

7. Who are the only two players to have scored 30,000 points in their NBA careers?

8. That night in the 1961-62 season when Wilt Chamberlain scored 78 points, another Hall-of-Famer scored 63 points in the same game. Name him.

9. True or false: George Mikan never scored more than 60 points in a game.

10. At the time he retired, this player was the third highest scorer in NBA history. Yet, he never played high school basketball. Who was it?

1. *New York Knicks*

2. *1961-62 season*

3. *David Thompson*

4. *George Gervin*

5. *Bob Cousy*

6. *Pete Maravich*

7. *Wilt Chamberlain and Kareem Abdul-Jabbar*

8. *Elgin Baylor*

9. *False. He scored 61 points against Rochester in 1952.*

10. *Paul Arizin*

GET HIS NUMBER

Listed here are names of players who've had jerseys retired by their respective clubs. What were their numbers?

1. Tom Heinsohn, Celtics

2. Lou Hudson, Hawks

3. Austin Carr, Cavaliers

4. Willis Reed, Knicks

5. Bill Cunningham, 76ers

6. Oscar Robertson, Bucks

7. Wes Unseld, Bullets

8. Lenny Wilkens, Supersonics

9. Walt Frazier, Knicks

10. John Havlicek, Celtics

21 Answers

1. *15*
2. *23*
3. *34*
4. *19*
5. *32*
6. *1*
7. *41*
8. *19*
9. *10*
10. *17*

SHOWTIME

Test your knowledge of the Lakers.

1. In 1979, the Lakers had two first-round draft choices. LA took Magic Johnson with one. Who'd they select with the other?

2. Who holds the team record for points in one game?

3. How many points did this Laker score in that game? Bonus shot: What team fell victim to his scoring spree?

4. This former Laker once scored 100 points in a college game. Can you name the player and his school?

5. The Lakers set an NBA-record 33-game winning streak in the 1971-72 season. What team ended that streak?

6. The coach that season was also on the Brooklyn Dodgers' bench when Bobby Thomson hit "the shot heard 'round the world" in 1951. Name him.

7. Jerry West was the second player taken in the 1960 NBA draft. Who was first?

8. This former Minneapolis Laker played in the 1959 NBA championship series. He later pitched for the Yankees in the 1963 World Series. Who is he?

9. Only one Lakers coach has led a team into the All-Star Game in his rookie season. Can you name him?

10. What Lakers owner was responsible for moving the team from Minneapolis to Los Angeles?

1. *Brad Holland, UCLA*

2. *Elgin Baylor, 1960*

3. *71 (bonus shot: New York Knicks)*

4. *Frank Selvy, Furman*

5. *Milwaukee Bucks*

6. *Bill Sharman*

7. *Oscar Robertson*

8. *Steve Hamilton*

9. *Pat Riley, 1982*

10. *Bob Short*

CLOSE SHAVE
A former Kentucky All-American had his promising NBA career cut short when he was implicated in the point-shaving scandal of the early 1950's. His name: Ralph Beard.

PLAYING BY THE RULES

True or false?

1. Coaches are not permitted to talk to an official during any timeout.

2. Regular timeouts are 60 seconds long.

3. The rule book designates the number of basketballs available to each team for pre-game warmups.

4. A player is awarded 3 points if he is standing on the three-point line when he makes his shot.

5. On in-bounds plays, the 24-second clock does not start until an offensive player touches the ball.

6. Each team is entitled to seven timeouts during regulation as well as one 20-second timeout per half.

7. A player who attempts a field goal may not be the first to touch the ball if it fails to touch the backboard, rim, or another player.

8. Any player who shatters a backboard during a game is automatically ejected.

9. If the ball rebounds or passes behind the backboard in either direction, it is considered out of bounds.

10. A player has 15 seconds to attempt a free throw after the ref has handed him the ball.

1. *True*

2. *False. 100 seconds*

3. *True. 6 apiece*

4. *False*

5. *False. It starts when any player touches the ball.*

6. *True*

7. *True*

8. *False. He's charged with a technical.*

9. *True*

10. *False. 10 seconds.*

MARCH MADNESS

1. John Wooden won his first NCAA title in 1964. What school did UCLA beat in the final?

2. What two schools competed in the first NCAA championship game in 1939?

3. Who won the title?

4. This 1970 NCAA finalist was the first team to average over 100 points a game for the season. Name the school.

5. UCLA's seven-year reign as NCAA champs ended in 1974 with a double-overtime loss in the semi-final game. What school de-throned them?

6. That school went on to win the title that year. Who was their final victim?

7. The University of Cincinnati won 2 straight championships in 1961 and 1962. They beat the same team in the finals both times. Name the school.

8. The Bearcats' bid for a third crown was put into hibernation by this team in 1963.

9. The University of San Francisco won its second consecutive title in 1956 by beating what team?

10. Name the first black head coach to win an NCAA title.

1. *Duke*

2. *Oregon and Ohio State*

3. *Oregon, 46-33*

4. *Jacksonville*

5. *North Carolina State*

6. *Marquette*

7. *Ohio State*

8. *Loyola of Chicago*

9. *Iowa*

10. *John Thompson, Georgetown*

25

ROAD TRIP

These NBA franchises had their beginnings in other cities. Can you give us the original team names?

1. Philadelphia 76ers

2. Houston Rockets

3. San Antonio Spurs

4. Washington Bullets

5. Los Angeles Clippers

6. Golden State Warriors

7. Utah Jazz

8. Sacramento Kings

9. Los Angeles Lakers

10. Atlanta Hawks

1. *Syracuse Nationals*

2. *San Diego Rockets*

3. *Dallas Chaparrals in the ABA*

4. *Chicago Packers*

5. *Buffalo Braves*

6. *Philadelphia Warriors*

7. *New Orleans Jazz*

8. *Rochester Royals*

9. *Minneapolis Lakers*

10. *Tri-Cities Hawks*

MAN TO MAN

Can you name them?

1. This man can take credit for making the first 3-point shot in the NBA.

2. This man is the only one to win NCAA, NBA, and ABA scoring titles.

3. This man became the youngest player-coach in the NBA at the age of 24 in 1964.

4. This man coached his team to two NBA titles in his last two years as a player.

5. This man played on championship teams in Milwaukee and Los Angeles.

6. This man became the youngest player in NBA history when he signed with the Atlanta Hawks out of high school.

7. This man is an NBA Hall-of-Famer. He was also the ABA's first commissioner.

8. This man was Rookie of the Year with the New Jersey Nets in 1981-82.

9. This man was "Mr. Inside" to Jerry West's "Mr. Outside" with the Lakers.

10. This man was the first MVP of the ABA in 1968.

1. *Chris Ford*

2. *Rick Barry*

3. *Dave DeBusschere*

4. *Bill Russell*

5. *Kareem Abdul-Jabbar*

6. *Bill Willoughby*

7. *George Mikan*

8. *Buck Williams*

9. *Elgin Baylor*

10. *Connie Hawkins*

AUTHOR! AUTHOR!

Name the writers of the following books, using the clues given.

1. *Born to Coach: A Season with the New York Knicks* - It was enough to make him race for the Bluegrass State.

2. *On and Off the Court* - His real name is Arnold, but you can call him...

3. *Chocolate Thunder* - He spent most of his NBA career on the planet Lovetron.

4. *Life on the Run* - His running is now done in the political arena.

5. *Showtime: Inside the Lakers' Breakthrough Season* - After one season in the broadcast booth, he decided to take his show from Tinseltown to Broadway.

6. *Louie in Season* - The Big East coach who's known for his sweaters as much as his court knowledge.

7. *Drive: The Story of My Life* - He chauffeured himself to 3 straight MVP awards in the 1980's.

8. *A Will to Win* - His will led the Knicks to the 1969-70 championship.

9. *Go Up for Glory* - That he did as one of the top rebounders and defensive players in NBA history.

10. *Mr. Clutch* - The Lakers could always count on him to keep them in gear.

1. *Rick Pitino*

2. *Red Auerbach*

3. *Daryl Dawkins*

4. *Bill Bradley*

5. *Pat Riley*

6. *Lou Carnesecca*

7. *Larry Bird*

8. *Willis Reed*

9. *Bill Russell*

10. *Jerry West*

ON THE JOHN

In 1972, two people shared *Sports Illustrated's* Sportsman of the Year award. One of them was the first woman to ever be so honored- tennis star Billie Jean King. The co-winner was a college basketball coach. Do you know him?

Answer: John Wooden of UCLA

GIVE AND GO

Listed below are the last names of famous backcourt-frontcourt combos. The letters are in proper order, but the names have been combined. See if you can flush out the players.

example: APRACRHIIBSAHLD = Archibald and Parish

1. FRRAEZIEERD

2. SMTAOLCOKNTEON

3. CRUOSSUESLYL

4. TLHAOIMMBEAESR

5. RTOWBYEMRTASNON

6. JAOBDHULNJASBOBNAR

7. WCHOIWTEENS

8. WCHEAMBSERLTAIN

9. HWOALLLTIONNS

10. CHHAEYNEISER

1. *Frazier and Reed*

2. *Stockton and Malone*

3. *Cousy and Russell*

4. *Thomas and Laimbeer*

5. *Robertson and Twyman*

6. *Johnson and Abdul-Jabbar*

7. *White and Cowens*

8. *West and Chamberlain*

9. *Hollins and Walton*

10. *Chenier and Hayes*

SCHOOL DAYS

1. What Kentucky school set an NCAA record in 1982-83 with its 39th consecutive winning season?

2. He was the first coach to win 100 games at three different schools, topping the century mark at St. John's, North Carolina, and South Carolina. Name him.

3. What conference sent five teams to the NCAA Tournament and three teams to the NIT in 1983?

4. Who was the center on the champion Indiana team that went 32-0 in 1975-76?

5. Only one independent won the NCAA Tournament in the 1970's. What school was it?

6. Name the only man to have played on an NCAA champ and coached a team to the title.

7. What college did Julius Erving attend?

8. This player is given credit for being the first to shoot the ball with one hand. It happened in 1936. Who was it?

9. What team ended Kentucky's record 129-game home-court winning streak in 1955?

10. This Providence guard became the NCAA leader in career steals in 1991. Name him.

1. *Louisville*

2. *Frank McGuire*

3. *Big Ten*

4. *Kent Benson*

5. *Marquette*

6. *Bobby Knight, Ohio State and Indiana*

7. *Massachusetts*

8. *Hank Luisetti, Stanford*

9. *Georgia Tech*

10. *Eric Murdock*

ANOTHER BASKETBALL ALTERNATIVE

How well do you remember the American Basketball Association?

1. What team won the first ABA championship?

2. Who was the MVP in the first ABA All-Star Game?

3. In the last five years of the league, Artis Gilmore won four rebounding titles. Who won the other one?

4. These two teams applied for entry into the NBA in 1975. Name them.

5. Who was the first ABA rebounding leader?

6. This player averaged 28 points a game for Indiana University before leaving school to sign with the Pacers. Who was it?

7. True or false: Billy Cunningham led the league in scoring in 1972-73.

8. Name the team that won three ABA championships.

9. This Kentucky All-American stayed in-state to play in the ABA. He led the league in scoring in his rookie year. Who was it?

10. Name the only three teams to make it through the stay of the ABA without the franchise being moved.

1. *Pittsburgh Pipers*

2. *Larry Brown*

3. *Swen Nater*

4. *Denver Nuggets and New York Nets*

5. *Mel Daniels*

6. *George McGinniss*

7. *True*

8. *Indiana Pacers*

9. *Dan Issel*

10. *Kentucky, Denver, and Indiana*

WHAT'S IN A NAME?

Name the players with these nicknames.

1. The Iceman

2. Sweetwater

3. The Chief

4. Pistol Pete

5. Harry the Horse

6. The Big E

7. Tiny

8. Dollar Bill

9. Truck

10. Chet the Jet

1. *George Gervin*

2. *Nat Clifton*

3. *Robert Parish*

4. *Pete Maravich*

5. *Harry Gallatin*

6. *Elvin Hayes*

7. *Nate Archibald*

8. *Bill Bradley*

9. *Leonard Robinson*

10. *Chet Walker*

THOUGHTS OF THE THRONE

It takes more than a sharp name to make it in the pros. Take Charles Edge, for instance. Nick-named "Razor", he lasted two years in the ABA. And Gene Gillette scored 8 points in 14 games for the 1946-47 Washington Capitals.

ON THE MARK

Name them.

1. The first center to lead the NBA in scoring and rebounding.

2. X marks the spot for the first collegian to lead the nation in scoring and rebounding in the same season (1984-85).

3. He scored a record 33 points in one quarter in the 1977-78 season.

4. This franchise can take credit for having the most individual scoring champions.

5. He's the all-time Celtics scoring leader.

6. The former Princeton guard who led the NBA and ABA in 3-point field goal percentage.

7. He's the only center to score 20,000 points in his career without being named to the first or second All-NBA teams.

8. His basket with two seconds left gave Boston a 108-107 win over the 76ers in the seventh game of the 1962 Eastern Division final.

9. This Hall-of-Famer was the first guard to average 30 points a game in a season.

10. He set an ABA record with the Carolina Cougars when he scored 67 points in one game during the 1971-72 season.

1. *Neil Johnston, Philadelphia Warriors*

2. *Xavier McDaniel, Wichita State*

3. *George Gervin, San Antonio*

4. *Philadelphia-San Francisco-Golden State Warriors*

5. *John Havlicek*

6. *Brian Taylor*

7. *Walt Bellamy*

8. *Sam Jones*

9. *Oscar Robertson*

10. *Larry Miller*

MATCH-UP ZONE

Shoot over the zone by matching the number with its significance.

1.	22	a	NBA all-time low for wins in a season
2.	69	b.	Billy Cunningham's uniform number
3.	11	c.	NBA record winning streak
4.	32	d.	games in NBA regular season
5.	16	e.	Elgin Baylor's uniform number
6.	9	f.	NCAA record winning streak
7.	17	g.	championship teams Bill Russell played on
8.	33	h.	NBA record for wins in a season
9.	82	i.	width (in feet) of foul lane in NBA
10.	88	j.	John Havlicek's uniform number

1. *e*

2. *h*

3. *g*

4. *b*

5. *i*

6. *a*

7. *j*

8. *c*

9. *d*

10. *f*

THE BIG DANCE

Listed below are the nicknames of NCAA champions. Tell us the school names.

1. Cardinals

2. Wolverines

3. Dons

4. Bruins

5. Wolfpack

6. Explorers

7. Bearcats

8. Warriors

9. Miners

10. Hoyas

1. *Louisville*

2. *Michigan*

3. *San Francisco*

4. *UCLA*

5. *North Carolina State*

6. *LaSalle*

7. *Cincinnati*

8. *Marquette*

9. *Texas Western*

10. *Georgetown*

THROUGH THE EIGHTIES

1. Who was the only man to win Coach of the Year twice in the decade?

2. He was the most valuable in the ABA three times, but he won his only NBA MVP award in 1980-81. Who was he?

3. This superstar soared to Rookie of the Year honors in the 1984-85 season, but missed 64 games the following year with a broken foot. Do you know? Do you know? Do you know?

4. Name the center who won rebounding titles with 2 different teams in the 80's.

5. This former Notre Dame star was the only player besides Michael Jordan to win more than one scoring race in the decade.

6. It took a 1983 order from the state legislature to get these intra-state schools to play each other on a regular basis. Name the state and the schools.

7. Three centers won the Rookie of the Year award during the 80's. Who were they?

8. Acquired by Detroit from Cleveland in 1981-82, this "bad boy" won the rebounding crown in the 1985-86 season. Name him.

9. Who was named Coach of the Year only once despite winning three NBA titles?

10. What expansion team entered the league in the 1980-81 season?

1. *Don Nelson, Milwaukee Bucks, 1983 and 1985*

2. *Julius Erving*

3. *Michael Jordan*

4. *Moses Malone, Houston (1980-81) and Philadelphia (1981-85)*

5. *Adrian Dantley*

6. *Kentucky; Kentucky and Louisville*

7. *Ralph Sampson (83-84), Patrick Ewing (85-86), and David Robinson (89-90)*

8. *Bill Laimbeer*

9. *Pat Riley, Lakers*

10. *Dallas Mavericks*

PARQUET PUZZLER

Test your luck on the Celtics.

1. Despite starting his career as the sixth man, this Hall-of-Famer went on to play in 13 All-Star Games. Who is he?

2. Bill Russell was the second player selected in the 1956 draft. Who did Rochester take instead with the first pick?

3. Who's the former Celtic who went on to become the only coach to win championships in three professional leagues?

4. In 1980, the Celtics traded the No. 1 pick in the draft to Golden State for Robert Parish and the third overall selection. Who did Boston take with that pick?

5. Name the player Golden State drafted with that No. 1 pick.

6. This Celtics Hall-of-Famer was the first player to lead the NBA in assists for three consecutive years. What's his name?

7. He wasn't the first player drafted by the Celtics in 1956, but he was the NBA's Rookie of the Year that season. Can you name him?

8. In 1980, Celtics coach Bill Fitch was Coach of the Year. With what other team did Fitch win that award?

9. What one-time Celtics coach has an MVP award for the 1973 All-Star Game in his trophy case?

10. True or false: Bill Russell never scored 50 points in a game in the NBA.

1. *John Havlicek*

2. *Si Green, Duquesne*

3. *Bill Sharman, in the NBA, ABA, and the American Basketball League*

4. *Kevin McHale*

5. *Joe Barry Carroll*

6. *Bob Cousy*

7. *Tom Heinsohn*

8. *Cleveland Cavaliers, 1976*

9. *Dave Cowens*

10. *True*

PICK AND ROLL

1. Who was the first commissioner of the NBA?

2. Dolph Schayes led this team to the playoffs every year between 1950 and 1963. Name the team.

3. Who was the first woman to play for the Harlem Globetrotters?

4. This Warrior averaged 40.8 points a game in the 1966-67 NBA Finals. Can you name him?

5. At the age of 42, he was the oldest to play in the NBA.

6. What team won the NBA title the first year after the merger with the ABA?

7. What two teams each appeared three times in the NBA Finals in the 1970's?

8. The lowest scoring game in NBA history occurred in 1950 when the Fort Wayne Pistons won, 19-18, over what team?

9. What NBA expansion team was the only one to qualify for the playoffs in its first season?

10. Thirteen was a lucky number for this player when he recorded 13 points, 13 assists, and 13 rebounds in the last game of the 1981-82 finals. Who was it?

1. *Maurice Podoloff*

2. *Syracuse Nationals*

3. *Lynette Woodard*

4. *Rick Barry*

5. *Kareem Abdul-Jabbar*

6. *Portland Trailblazers*

7. *Knicks and Bullets*

8. *Minneapolis Lakers*

9. *Chicago Bulls*

10. *Magic Johnson*

TRIVIQUATIONS

Test your math and your hoops knowledge. Fill in the number portion of the answers suggested by the clues and solve the Triviquation.

1. (Charles Barkley's number + Walt Frazier's number) x halves in a game = UCLA's record winning streak

2. $\dfrac{\text{seconds in shot clock}}{\text{NBA roster size}}$ + Kareem's retirement age = Jerry West's number

3. Total NBA teams + height of rim = total points in NBA's lowest scoring game

4. $\dfrac{\text{Patrick Ewing's number}}{\text{Lakers' winning streak}}$ + $\dfrac{\text{Central Division teams}}{\text{Pacific Division teams}}$ = rounds in NBA draft

5. shots in technical foul + Knick scoring champs x Magic's number = teams in NCAA tournament

1. $(34 + 10) \times 2 = 88$

2. $\dfrac{24}{12} + 42 = 44$

3. $27 + 10 = 37$

4. $\dfrac{33}{33} + \dfrac{7}{7} = 2$

5. $1 + 1 \times 32 = 64$

STICKIN' THE J

The answers to these questions are all players whose last names begin with the letter "J".

1. He played on 3 NBA champs with 2 different teams and was the 1979 Playoff MVP with Seattle.

2. This pro led the ABA in blocked shots in 1973-74 and 1974-75 before playing for five different NBA teams.

3. Laker guard who has led the NBA in assists four times and was MVP three times in the 80's.

4. Known primarily for his offensive skills, he was also the NBA's Defensive Player of the Year in 1987-88.

5. Phoenix acquired this point guard in a trade with Cleveland. He was a starter in the 1991 All-Star Game.

6. Teamed with K.C. in the Boston backcourt. Also played on ten NBA champions.

7. He led the NBA in scoring from 1953 to 1955, becoming the first player to do so three straight years.

8. A No. 1 draft pick out of St. John's, he was the 1987-88 Rookie of the Year.

9. Known for his defense, he was the valuable sixth man on the 76ers 1982-83 title-winning team.

10. The champion Pistons' "Microwave."

1. *Dennis Johnson*

2. *Caldwell Jones*

3. *Magic Johnson*

4. *Michael Jordan*

5. *Kevin Johnson*

6. *Sam Jones*

7. *Neil Johnston*

8. *Mark Jackson*

9. *Bobby Jones*

10. *Vinnie Johnson*

THE FINAL FOUR

1. This coach made five trips to the Final Four in his career, yet never won. Who was it?

2. The University of San Francisco won the first of its two straight titles in 1955. Who'd they beat in the final game?

3. A future NBA Hall-of-Famer set a tournament record for rebounds in a game when he snared 31 boards for Bowling Green in 1963. Can you name him?

4. In 1957, North Carolina won two straight triple-overtime games on its way to the championship. One was against Kansas in the final. Who was the other victim?

5. Only two freshmen have been named the tournament's Most Outstanding Player. Arnie Ferrin of Utah did it in 1944. You name the other frosh winner.

6. This athlete played in the 1963 Final Four. Earlier in the school year, he had a 99-yard TD run in the Liberty Bowl and also won the Heisman Trophy. Who was it?

7. The 1976 NCAA champ has the distinction of being the first team to win the title with five black starters. Can you name the school?

8. Give yourself extra credit if you can name the loser of that year's title game.

9. His basket with sixteen seconds left in the 1982 final game lifted his team to the championship over Georgetown. The player and his school, please.

10. This national championship game had the highest TV ratings of any final game. Do you know which one? (Hint: The team from Indiana was not the Hoosiers, while the team from Michigan was not the Wolverines.)

1. *Guy Lewis, Houston*

2. *LaSalle*

3. *Nate Thurmond*

4. *Michigan State in the semi-final game*

5. *Pervis Ellison, Louisville, 1986*

6. *Terry Baker, Oregon State*

7. *Texas Western (now Texas El-Paso)*

8. *Kentucky*

9. *Michael Jordan, North Carolina*

10. *The 1979 game between Michigan St. (led by Magic Johnson) and Indiana St. (led by Larry Bird). Michigan St. won.*

HOME COURT ADVANTAGE

Name the home courts of these teams.

1. Minnesota Timberwolves

2. Chicago Bulls

3. Indiana Pacers

4. Charlotte Hornets

5. Milwaukee Bucks

6. Utah Jazz

7. Boston Celtics

8. Denver Nuggets

9. Portland Trailblazers

10. Sacramento Kings

1. *Target Center*

2. *Chicago Stadium*

3. *Market Square Arena*

4. *Charlotte Coliseum*

5. *Bradley Center*

6. *Salt Palace*

7. *Boston Garden*

8. *McNichols Sports Arena*

9. *Memorial Coliseum*

10. *ARCO Arena*

MOONLIGHTING

Consider giving up that day job if you can make it through this game without a turnover.

1. He played with the Celtics, Brooklyn Dodgers, and Chicago Cubs, but is best known for his shot on "The Rifleman."

2. This former Lakers coach was an 11th round pick of the Dallas Cowboys in the 1967 NFL draft.

3. The "hot corner" was too hot for him, so he left the Toronto Blue Jays to play full time in the NBA.

4. This cracker-jack quarterback made it to the NFL Hall of Fame, but not before playing the 1945-46 season with the Rochester Royals.

5. The Detroit Pistons can lay claim to having two major league pitchers on their roster. One was Dave DeBusschere. You name the other hurler.

6. The defensive lineman from Michigan State that was the first pick of the 1967 NFL draft was also the 11th round pick of the Bullets that year.

7. The Kansas City Kings thought enough of this Olympic gold-medal winner to select him in the 7th round of the 1977 draft. Do you know the decathlete?

8. You're good if you can name the Pro Football Hall of Fame defensive back who played for Toledo in the 1943 NIT and for the Giants and Packers in the NFL.

9. You're better if you can identify the athlete from NYU who led his team in scoring in the 1943 NCAA Tournament and later managed the Minnesota Twins in the World Series.

10. Give the boss two weeks notice if you can name the athlete who played for the NBA St. Louis Hawks in the 1955-56 season, and pitched for the baseball St. Louis Cardinals in the 1959 season. No peeking at the answer.

1. *Chuck Connors*

2. *Pat Riley*

3. *Danny Ainge*

4. *Otto Graham*

5. *Ron Reed*

6. *Bubba Smith*

7. *Bruce Jenner*

8. *Emlen Tunnell*

9. *Sam Mele*

10. *Dick Ricketts (you peeked)*

ON THE JOHN
This sportscaster and former NBA player, when asked how he would guard Kareem Abdul-Jabbar said, "I'd get real close to him and breathe on his goggles." Can you name this John? (Hint: he once held the NBA record for most consecutive games played.)

Answer: Johnny Kerr

THREE-PEAT

Each player listed at the bottom has won an NBA scoring title. One, though, did it 3 straight years. His name is omitted from this puzzle. Find the answer through the process of elimination. Names can be found horizontally, vertically, frontwards, and backwards - but always in a straight line.

```
D L A B I H C R A E T A N P R U
A O P A B L F E T D L R E G N T
V F M S E W I A R B C T K A S M
E X L I R Z P D Q F E V Y E B O
B R A N N U T S I M B M W X Y T
I J C L A I X N A Y T N O L Z
N H A F R L Q R B J R A H V C E
G E L Y D H A U L R S K Y P A L
O R T A K V T M E N H Z R G D V
A G P W I E R J D W C O R P L I
R M O C N C L T S G I F A T V N
E B H I G D Y Z H W A L B E M H
W A S H U P B N L P Y U K L O A
O R E T T E L D E R O S C I L Y
H A L E X E N G L I S H I O N E
S H A V E C T O P U G T R T I S
```

Rick Barry
Dave Bing
Bob McAdoo
Jerry West
Bernard King

Pete Maravich
Nate Archibald
Alex English
Dominique Wilkins
Elvin Hayes

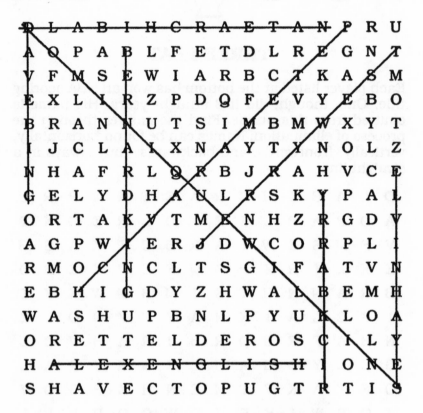

D L A B I H C R A E T A N P R U
A Q P A B L F E T D L R E G N T
V F M S E W I A R B C T K A S M
E X L I R Z P D Q F E V Y E B O
B R A N U T S I M B M W X Y T
I J C L A X N A Y T N O L Z
N H A F R L Q R B J R A H V C E
G E L Y D H A U L R S K Y P A L
O R T A K V T M N H Z R G D V
A G P W E R J D W C O R P L I
R M O C N C L T S G I F A T V N
E B H I G D Y Z H W A L B E M H
W A S H U P B N L P Y U L O A
O R E T T E L D E R O S C I L Y
H A L E X E N G L I S H I O N E
S H A V E C T O P U G T R T I S

Rick Barry	Pete Maravich
Dave Bing	Nate Archibald
Bob McAdoo	Alex English
Jerry West	Dominique Wilkins
Bernard King	Elvin Hayes

ANSWER: Bob McAdoo

20-SECOND TIMEOUT

Take a breather...but not too long. Twenty seconds is all you should need to give us the nicknames of these players.

1. Oscar Robertson

2. Hakeem Olajuwon

3. Walt Frazier

4. Michael Jordan

5. Julius Erving

6. Karl Malone

7. Jerry West

8. Eric Floyd

9. John Williams

10. Hersey Hawkins

1. *The Big "O"*

2. *The Dream*

3. *Clyde*

4. *Air*

5. *Dr. J*

6. *The Mailman*

7. *Mr. Clutch*

8. *Sleepy*

9. *Hot Rod*

10. *The Hawk*

THE LOW POST

1. Only two players besides Wilt Chamberlain and Bill Russell have grabbed 40 or more rebounds in a game. Who are they?

2. This center led his team to a franchise-high 56 wins in 1989-90 while performing "admirably" as Rookie of the Year. Who was it?

3. Michael Jordan was the second pick in the 1984 draft. Portland chose this pivot man with the No. 1 selection. Name him.

4. Can you name the center, other than Wilt Chamberlain, to win Rookie of the Year and MVP awards in the same season?

5. Despite an injury-marred career, this redhead won the league's MVP Award as well as the 1977 NBA Finals MVP. Name him.

6. He won the scoring and rebounding titles on his way to the 1955-56 MVP Award. Who is this Hawk?

7. Who were Houston's "Twin Towers?"

8. Name the Celtics center who was co-Rookie of the Year in 1970-71, MVP in 1972-73, All-Star MVP in 1973, and Hall-of-Famer in 1991.

9. Wilt Chamberlain led the NBA in rebounding four straight years. But this player did it five consecutive times in the 1980's. Name him.

10. What center was named to the All-NBA team 15 times, most of any player?

1. *Jerry Lucas and Nate Thurmond*

2. *David Robinson*

3. *Sam Bowie*

4. *Wes Unseld*

5. *Bill Walton*

6. *Bob Pettit*

7. *Hakeem Olajuwon and Ralph Sampson*

8. *Dave Cowens*

9. *Moses Malone*

10. *Kareem Abdul-Jabbar*

ALMA MATER

Match the Hall of Fame player with the college he attended.

1.	Cliff Hagan	a.	LSU
2.	Jerry Lucas	b.	Holy Cross
3.	Billy Cunningham	c.	Grambling
4.	George Mikan	d.	Kentucky
5.	Tom Heinsohn	e.	LaSalle
6.	Dave DeBusschere	f.	DePaul
7.	Pete Maravich	g.	Ohio State
8.	K.C. Jones	h.	Detroit
9.	Willis Reed	i.	North Carolina
10.	Tom Gola	j.	San Francisco

1. *d*
2. *g*
3. *i*
4. *f*
5. *b*
6. *h*
7. *a*
8. *j*
9. *c*
10. *e*

KNICK KNACKS

1. Oscar Robertson and Jerry West were the first two players picked in the 1960 draft. Who was the California center the Knicks chose with the third pick?

2. Name the only Knick to win an NBA scoring title.

3. This Knick once scored 57 points in a game in 1959. Later he went on to coach the Hawks. Who is he?

4. Who was the New York guard who led the NBA in steals and assists in 1979-80?

5. Who replaced Dick McGuire as coach of the Knickerbockers?

6. This Knick Hall-of-Famer was named MVP in the All-Star Game, the regular season, and the playoffs during the 1969-70 season. Name him.

7. The Knicks acquired Dave DeBusschere from Detroit for what two players?

8. This Hall-of-Famer averaged 20 rebounds a game twice in his career. He wound up on the NBA's list of top ten career rebounders. Who is he?

9. What Knick guard set an NBA playoff record, handing off 19 assists in the final game of the 1969-70 championship series?

10. This player came to the Knicks from the Harlem Globetrotters. Do you know his name?

1. *Darrall Imhoff*

2. *Bernard King, 1984-85*

3. *Richie Guerin*

4. *Michael Ray Richardson*

5. *Red Holzman*

6. *Willis Reed*

7. *Walt Bellamy and Butch Komives*

8. *Jerry Lucas*

9. *Walt Frazier*

10. *Nat "Sweetwater" Clifton*

FOUR-LETTER MEN

The answers to these clues are all four-letter last names.

1. A North Carolina product, he was NBA Rookie of the Year in 1978-79.

2. He was the shortest player in the NBA until Muggsy Bogues arrived on the scene.

3. Laker great and 12 times All-NBA, he won a scoring title in 1969-70 and an assist crown in 1971-72.

4. Rookie of the Year in 1964-65 for the Knicks.

5. In 1989 he became the first No. 1 draft pick in the history of the Charlotte Hornets.

6. The Piston guard who followed a Rookie of the Year season by winning the scoring title in 1967-68, his second year.

7. Said, "Arrivaderci, Boston," to play the 1989-90 season in Italy.

8. Named Outstanding Player in the 1989 NCAA Tournament, he was the first draft pick of the Miami Heat.

9. Played in three All-Star Games with three different teams - Golden State, New York, and Washington.

10. The "Hick from French Lick."

1. *Phil Ford*

2. *Spud Webb*

3. *Jerry West*

4. *Willis Reed*

5. *J.R. Reid*

6. *Dave Bing*

7. *Brian Shaw*

8. *Glen Rice*

9. *Bernard King*

10. *Larry Bird*

THOUGHTS OF THE THRONE

He won the Red Auerbach Trophy as Coach of the Year for the 1973-74 season, improving the Detroit Pistons record to 52-30 from the previous year's 40-42 mark. Who is he? (Hint: his last name is the same as a leading toilet paper manufacturer.)

Answer: Ray Scott

FULL COURT PRESS

1. The NBA established a new rule for the 1954-55 season that changed the way the game was played. What was the innovation?

2. He set an NBA record when he played in 906 consecutive games. Who is he?

3. This player, though, played in 1,041 straight games in the ABA and NBA. Can you name him?

4. Because he was traded from the Knicks to the Pistons in the middle of the 1968-69 season, this man played in 88 regular season games. Who was it?

5. What team won the last ABA championship in 1976?

6. Two players have the distinction of playing on the NBA's winningest team (the '71-'72 Lakers) and the team with the lowest winning percentage (the '72-'73 76ers). Who were they?

7. Isiah Thomas was the second player chosen in the 1981 draft. Who was the first?

8. This team brought home a road record of 0-20 during the 1953-54 season. Name this gang that couldn't shoot straight.

9. What team lost the coin flip with Milwaukee for the right to draft Lew Alcindor in 1969?

10. What player did they take with that second pick?

1. *the 24-second clock*

2. *Randy Smith*

3. *Ron Boone*

4. *Walt Bellamy*

5. *New York Nets*

6. *Leroy Ellis and John Q. Trapp*

7. *Mark Aguirre*

8. *Baltimore Bullets*

9. *Phoenix Suns*

10. *Neal Walk*

THE SHOT AT THE BUZZER

These former players are listed with the team with which their careers ended. Can you name the teams that made them No. 1 draft picks?

1. Pete Maravich, Celtics

2. Dave DeBusschere, Knicks

3. Maurice Lucas, Trailblazers

4. Bobby Jones, 76ers

5. Otis Birdsong, Nets

6. Jerry Sloan, Bulls

7. Butch Beard, Knicks

8. Nate Thurmond, Cavaliers

9. Gail Goodrich, Jazz

10. Bill Walton, Celtics

1. *Atlanta Hawks, 1970*

2. *Detroit Pistons, 1962*

3. *Chicago Bulls, 1974*

4. *Houston Rockets, 1974*

5. *Kansas City Kings, 1977*

6. *Baltimore Bullets, 1965*

7. *Atlanta Hawks, 1969*

8. *San Francisco Warriors, 1963*

9. *Los Angeles Lakers, 1965*

10. *Portland Trailblazers, 1974*

The Bathroom Library

THE BATHROOM BASKETBALL BOOK
THE BATHROOM GUEST BOOK
THE BATHROOM CROSSWORD PUZZLE BOOK
THE BATHROOM DIGEST
THE BATHROOM TRIVIA BOOK
THE BATHROOM ENTERTAINMENT BOOK
THE BATHROOM SPORTS QUIZ BOOK
THE BATHROOM SPORTS QUOTE BOOK
THE BATHROOM GAME BOOK
THE BATHROOM BASEBALL BOOK
THE BATHROOM FOOTBALL BOOK
THE BATHROOM GOLF BOOK
THE BATHROOM SOAP OPERA BOOK
THE BATHROOM INSPIRATION BOOK

For further information, write to:
Red-Letter Press, Inc.
P.O. Box 393,
Saddle River, N.J. 07458